Collins

Easy Learning

KS3
English
Workbook

Levels 3–7

Lucy English

About this book

This book has been written to help you prepare for your Key Stage 3 English test at the end of Year 9. It contains all the practice you need to do well in the reading, writing and Shakespeare papers.

The book is divided into three sections corresponding to the three papers. It includes test-style practice questions, mock test papers and a revision checklist for each section.

For more specific information on how to use this book, please see the following pages:

- **reading:** pages 4–5
- **writing:** pages 42–3
- **Shakespeare:** pages 78–9

How to check your answers

You can check your answers for FREE by visiting **www.collinseducation.com/easylearning** where full mark and level guidance is also given in an easy-to-download format.

Revision and practice

Use Collins *Easy Learning KS3 English Revision Levels 3–5* and *Easy Learning KS3 English Revision Levels 6–7* alongside this Workbook to prepare yourself fully for the tests. You can revise the topic in the revision books and then test yourself by answering the questions in this Workbook.

Published by Collins
An imprint of HarperCollins*Publishers*
77 – 85 Fulham Palace Road
Hammersmith
London W6 8JB

Browse the complete Collins catalogue at
www.collins.co.uk

© HarperCollins*Publishers* Limited 2007
First published in 2006
This new edition published in 2007

10 9 8 7 6 5 4

ISBN-13 978-0-00-726569-5

Lucy English asserts her moral right to be identified as the author of this work.

British Library Cataloguing in Publication Data
A Catalogue record for this publication is available from the British Library

Written by Lucy English
Edited by Sue Chapple
Design by Sally Boothroyd
Illustrations by Kathy Baxendale, Harriet Buckley, Linzie Hunter, Andy Tudor, David Whittle
Printed and bound by Martins the Printers Ltd

Acknowledgements
The Publishers gratefully acknowledge the following for permission to reproduce copyright material:
Text © 2005 Anthony Horowitz
Extract from RAVEN'S GATE by Anthony Horowitz
Reproduced by permission of Walker Books Ltd, London SE11 5HJ.
Extract from *The Boy in the Striped Pyjamas* by John Boyne, published by David Fickling Books. Reprinted by permission of The Random House Group Ltd.
'Acting Out' in the *Woking Magazine*, Summer 2005. Reprinted with permission.
'Blackberry Picking' from *Death of a Naturalist* by Seamus Heaney, Faber and Faber Ltd.
Extract from *An Arrest* by Ambrose Bierce in *The New Windmill Book of Nineteenth Century Short Stories* by n/a. Reprinted by permission of Harcourt Education.
'Shades of Red' in *The Donor* magazine, Copyright © National Blood Service

Photographs
The Author and Publishers are grateful to the following for permission to reproduce photographs:
l = left, *r* = right
p. 10 *Woking Magazine*, Summer 2005.
p. 14 LWA-Dann Tardif/Corbis.
p. 21 Photos.com
p. 24 Bureau L.A. Collection/Corbis. © TM. Aardman Animations Ltd. 2005. All Rights Reserved.
p. 29 David MacCarthy/Science Photo Library.
p. 30 and p. 31 *The Donor* magazine, Copyright © National Blood Service.
p. 32 *l* CNRI/Science Photo Library, *r* Andrew Syred/Science Photo Library.
p. 53 Brigitte Sporrer/zefa/Corbis.

Whilst every effort has been made to trace the copyright holders, in cases where this has been unsuccessful, or if any have inadvertently been overlooked, the Publishers will be pleased to make the necessary arrangements at the first opportunity.

Contents

The reading paper

The key things you need to know

This Workbook contains ten practice texts for you to work through. It doesn't matter how long you spend on them – in fact, it's better to take the time you need to make sure your answers are brilliant! If you want to check your own answers, you will find instructions on the inside back cover.

When you've worked through all the practice texts, have a go at the mock test paper. Try to do this in proper test conditions and spend 1 hour and 15 minutes on it. You will need someone to time you (don't forget the 15 minutes reading and note making before you open the question section). There are 32 marks available so try to get every one of them. Again, you can check your own answers.

The texts

We have used a variety of texts in this Workbook, just as you will find in the real test. The first thing you need to do when you read each one is to work out the **purpose**, **audience** and **text type**. This isn't a task that gains marks, but it will help you with the questions that follow. It's really good to get into the habit of using this skill whenever you are reading or writing.

The questions

There are up to six questions on each practice text. They tell you how many marks are available for each question – don't forget to match your answer to this number. The number of lines available will also be a good indication.

The questions test the Reading Assessment Focuses (AF 2–6); just as they will in the real thing you'll sit in May:

AF2: understand, describe, select or retrieve information, events or ideas from texts and use quotation and reference to text

This means you need to show you understand what you have read by picking ideas and evidence out of the text. You can also put events and ideas in your own words.

AF3: deduce, infer or interpret information, events or ideas from texts

This means you can make links between ideas. You read between the lines and work out the story or idea that is implied.

AF4: identify and comment on the structure and organisation of texts, including grammatical and presentational features at text level

This means you can explain how and why the text is structured in the way it is. This might refer to layout or how the writing develops.

AF5: explain and comment on writers' use of language, including grammatical and literary features at word and sentence level

This means you can write about the language of the text and explain why certain words or phrases have been used and the effect they have on the reader.

AF6: identify and comment on writers' purposes and viewpoints and the overall effect of the text on the reader

This means you can look at the big picture – you can explain why the writer has written the text and what they were trying to do. You can also explain what impact the whole text has on the reader.

Answering the questions in the test paper

• When it comes to the real test, start at the beginning and **work your way through** the questions in order. If you get stuck, move on to the next question, but try to go back later and write something – you may get some marks for it and it's better than leaving a blank space.

• **Do exactly what you are asked**. If you are asked to write a word or phrase, don't write an essay.

• Look at the **marks** given for each question, and the **space** provided in the answer booklet. They will give you an idea about how much you should write.

• When commenting or explaining, **use quotation** in your answer. If you can pick a word or phrase from the text to support your ideas it shows you are an accurate and precise reader. (That's a good thing!)

Timing the test paper

• Time your 15 minutes reading time carefully. Read the texts and try to work out **purpose**, **audience**, **text type**.

• You have **1 hour** to answer all the questions. That means about 20 minutes for the questions on each text.

• Use the **marks** as a guide to how long to spend on a question. You shouldn't spend more than 2 minutes per mark.

• Leave 5 minutes at the end to read through and **check** your answers.

Good luck!

1

Read the extract and answer the questions that follow.

This is the opening of a book called *Raven's Gate*, by Anthony Horowitz.

Matt Freeman knew he was making a mistake.

He was sitting on a low wall outside Ipswich station, wearing a grey hooded sweatshirt, shapeless, faded jeans, and trainers with frayed laces. It was six o'clock in the evening and the London train had just pulled in. Behind him, commuters were fighting their way out of the station. The concourse was a tangle of cars, taxis and pedestrians, all of them trying to find their way home. A traffic light blinked from red to green but nothing moved. Somebody leant on their horn and the noise blared out, cutting through the damp evening air. Matt heard it and looked up briefly. But the crowd meant nothing to him. He wasn't part of it. He never had been – and he sometimes thought he never would be.

Getting to grips with the text

• Purpose = _____

• Audience = _____

• Text type = _____

1   Matt is made to seem an outsider. Find one quotation that shows he does not fit in.

_____

_____

1 mark

2   How does the structure of the extract emphasise Matt's isolation?

_____

_____

_____

_____

2 marks

3 The table below gives examples of descriptive language used in the text.
Complete the table to explain the impression each word or phrase gives.

Example of descriptive language	The impression it gives
'commuters were fighting their way out of the station'	This gives the impression of pressure and chaos.
'a tangle of cars, taxis and pedestrians'	
'Somebody leant on their horn and the noise blared out'	

2 marks

4 The extract emphasises Matt's feeling of isolation and not belonging.
Explain how the whole extract creates this impression.
Support your ideas with quotations from the extract.

_____

_____

_____

_____

_____

_____

_____

_____

_____

3 marks

5 What sort of thing do you think might happen next? Provide evidence for
your answer.

_____

_____

_____

_____

_____

_____

_____

2 marks

2

Read the extract and answer the questions that follow.

> This is from a book called *The Boy in the Striped Pyjamas*, by John Boyne. It is about a nine-year-old boy called Bruno.
>
> Bruno narrowed his eyes and wished he were taller, stronger and eight years older. A ball of anger exploded inside him and made him wish that he had the courage to say exactly what he wanted to say. It was one thing, he decided, to be told what to do by Mother and Father – that was perfectly reasonable and to be expected – but it was another thing entirely to be told what to do by someone else. Even by someone with a fancy title like 'Lieutenant'.

Getting to grips with the text

- Purpose = _____

- Audience = _____

- Text type = _____

1 Why is Bruno angry?

_____

2 The writer describes the way Bruno is feeling very clearly. Identify two words or phrases that show his anger.

_____

_____

3 Complete the table, explaining what each of these quotations tells us about Bruno's state of mind.

Quotation	What it tells us about Bruno's state of mind
'Bruno narrowed his eyes and wished he were taller, stronger and eight years older'	
'A ball of anger exploded inside him'	

4 What is Bruno's attitude towards the Lieutenant? Provide a quotation to support your answer.

_____

_____

_____

1 mark

5 Bruno refers to his parents as 'Mother' and 'Father'. Why does this make him seem young?

_____

_____

_____

2 marks

6 The writer makes us take Bruno's side in this extract. How has he done this?

_____

_____

_____

_____

_____

_____

_____

_____

_____

_____

_____

_____

_____

_____

_____

_____

_____

_____

5 marks

3

Read the extract and answer the questions that follow.

 # Acting Out

Young people can take centre stage this summer with Woking Borough Council's arts workshops.

Calling all budding actors and artists! There is a packed programme of activities lined up this summer to get your creative juices really flowing.

If you fancy yourself as an actor, why not join one of the **drama workshops** at the Rhonda McGaw theatre? These will give you a chance to develop your theatre skills while exploring some exciting scripts from top writers including Salman Rushdie and Timberlake Wertenbaker.

You'll have lots of fun learning new skills and meeting other young people with a flair for the stage. And you can show off your talents when you invite family and friends to a final performance at the end of the week.

Or if you'd like to see behind the screen at the Rhoda McGaw theatre, you can sign up for a **cinema crafts workshop** in August. You'll be able to make your own costumes and props for the show for the afternoon film. The workshops are suitable for children aged 7–11, and discounts for Passport to Leisure holders are available.

Crafty types aged between 7 and 11 can make their mark at **arts workshops** at Woking Youth Arts Centre, Knaphill, on 27th or 28th July. Try African drumming or make your own Mexican crafts at a Holiday Fiesta workshop – and take your creations home at the end of the day.

The Craft Co. will also be running workshops for children aged 6 and above at The Barn in Worplesdon throughout August. There's a huge range of activities available, including T-shirt painting, salt-dough modelling, card-making and pot-decorating.

Young dancers and poets aged between 8 and 16 have their chance to shine between 22nd and 26th August at Woking College Dance Studio.

Working with professional dancers, you can contribute your ideas to a new words and movement experience. Friends and family are welcome to watch the final performance on Friday afternoon.

- Purpose = _____

- Audience = _____

- Text type = _____

Getting to grips with the text

1 This article outlines summer activities for young people in Woking. Give one activity that will be available and some details of what it will include.

_____

_____

2 marks

2 The language used makes the opportunities sound exciting.
Complete the table to explain what the language suggests in each example.

Example of language used	What it suggests
'a packed programme'	The alliteration makes it sound fun and exciting.
'a huge range of activities'	
'chance to shine'	

2 marks

3 How does the whole article make the opportunities available for young people in Woking during the summer seem exciting and attractive?
You should comment on how the extract:
• Makes the activities seem exciting and fun
• Makes it seem easy to join, even if you don't know anyone
• Uses presentation and layout devices to help the reader find the information they might be interested in.

_____

_____

_____

_____

_____

_____

_____

_____

_____

_____

_____

_____

_____

_____

_____

_____

5 marks

4

Read the letter and answer the questions that follow.

LeisureTime Plus
Rock Hill Road
Sheffield
01234 567890

Dear Ms Holroyd,

Everybody knows the need to live a healthy lifestyle but did you know that regular exercise can boost your immune system and improve your energy levels by up to 50%? Experts have shown that people who exercise for just 30 minutes three times a week are fitter, healthier and happier. At LeisureTime Plus we want to help you reach this state.

Forget all you might think about crowded, sweaty gyms and sergeant-major fitness instructors with the bark of a bulldog; our staff and facilities are second to none and help to make exercise fun and rewarding. We're not saying it's going to be a walk in the park, but we'll be with you all the way as you travel your journey to a fitter, happier you.

Just think, in four weeks you'll notice your skin will have a new, radiant glow, in six weeks your jeans will be easier to do up, and in twelve weeks you'll be running up flights of stairs without a thought. Sound good? Well just sign up for our fabulous new introductory offer today and this could be your reality.

Call LeisureTime Plus today for more details, we're looking forward to helping find the new you.

Yours truly,

Malcolm Day

Director, LeisureTime Plus

- Purpose = _____
- Audience = _____
- Text type = _____

Getting to grips with the text

1 What does this letter want the reader to do?

_____

1 mark

2 The letter is addressed to a specific person, Ms Holroyd. What sort of person does the letter suggest Ms Holroyd is?

_____

_____

2 marks

3 Explain two different ways in which the letter makes exercise sound appealing.

• _____

• _____

2 marks

4 The letter uses negative phrases to describe bad fitness experiences.
Fill in the table to explain why the language is used in this way.

Example of negative phrase	Why the language is used in this way
'crowded, sweaty gyms'	
'sergeant-major fitness instructors with the bark of a bulldog'	

2 marks

5 The letter uses informal, colloquial phrases. Identify one of these phrases and explain why it is used.

• Informal, colloquial phrase: _____

• Why it is used: _____

2 marks

6 Explain how this letter makes joining LeisureTime Plus seem a good idea.
In your answer you should write about:
• The use of fact and opinion
• The tone of the letter
• The use of language.

_____
_____
_____
_____
_____
_____
_____
_____
_____
_____
_____
_____
_____
_____

5 marks

5

Read the newspaper article and answer the questions that follow.

SCHOOLKIDS TO BE GIVEN MOBILE PHONES
Government heralds a huge step forward in learning technology

Government ministers were celebrating yesterday after announcing a deal with mobile phone manufacturers to give these gadgets to all schoolchildren. They are confident the newest range of phones will help students learn in today's techno-world.

Wayne Daniels, advisor for education, said this move would enable children to interact with lessons in a modern way as they could be used as personal organisers and even record parts of lessons. "Students won't be able to claim they forgot to do their homework," he said, "not when it's recorded onto the phone's organiser with an alarm set for that evening."

Backers of this scheme reel off lists of benefits: students will be able to use the organiser, the memo facility,

research using the Internet, share ideas in class, manipulate sounds in music; there's even the alarm to get them up in the morning and prevent them being late for school!

However, teachers are questioning this move, claiming that phones are a nuisance, constantly interrupting lessons and providing a target for bullies and thieves. They demand to know how much money has been spent on this project, and suggest some of this could have been spent improving the many dilapidated school buildings around the country.

Students, meanwhile, were celebrating!

Getting to grips with the text

- Purpose = _____
- Audience = _____
- Text type = _____

1 Identify two ways that it is claimed mobile phones will help students' learning.

- _____
- _____

1 mark

2 How does the writer show that the teachers' views are going to be different from the views already described in the article?

_____

3 What does the phrase 'today's techno-world' suggest?

_____

_____

4 What is the effect of having a quotation from the education advisor?

_____

_____

5 Some of the language used in the paragraph about the teachers' response is very negative. Pick two negative words or phrases and explain the impression they create.

- _____

_____

_____

- _____

_____

_____

6 Does this article present all views in a balanced way? Use evidence to support your ideas.

_____

_____

_____

_____

_____

_____

_____

_____

_____

_____

_____

_____

Read the poem and answer the questions that follow.

> **Blackberry picking**
> (for Philip Hobsbaum)
> *by Seamus Heaney*
>
> Late August, given heavy rain and sun
> For a full week, the blackberries would ripen.
> At first, just one, a glossy purple clot
> Among others, red, green, hard as a knot.
> You ate that first one and its flesh was sweet
> Like thickened wine: summer's blood was in it
> Leaving stains upon the tongue and lust for
> Picking. Then red ones inked up and that hunger
> Sent us out with milk-cans, pea-tins, jam-pots
> Where briars scratched and wet grass bleached our boots.
> Round hayfields, cornfields and potato-drills
> We trekked and picked until the cans were full,
> Until the tinkling bottom had been covered
> With green ones, and on top big blobs burned
> Like a plate of eyes. Our hands were peppered
> With thorn pricks, our palms sticky as Bluebeard's.
>
> We hoarded the fresh berries in the byre.
> But when the bath was filled we found a fur,
> A rat-grey fungus, glutting on our cache.
> The juice was stinking too. Once off the bush
> The fruit fermented, the sweet flesh would turn sour.
> I always felt like crying. It wasn't fair
> That all the lovely canfuls smelt of rot.
> Each year I hoped they'd keep, knew they would not.

Bluebeard was a savage murderer who killed his first six wives.
briars = the long, thorny stems that blackberries grow on
cache = a collection, store or treasure

• Purpose = _____

• Audience = _____

• Text type = _____

Getting to grips with the text

1 The poem describes blackberry picking. Every year the narrator tries to pick and keep blackberries but isn't able to. What happens?

1 mark

_____

2 The narrator says they collected the blackberries in 'milk-cans, pea-tins, jam-pots'. What does this suggest about the blackberry collectors?

_____

1 mark

3 What is the impact of the final line?

_____

1 mark

4 Find and write down an example of a simile. Explain why the poet has used this image.

Simile: _____

1 mark

Explanation: _____

_____

_____

2 marks

5 The blackberry pickers work hard to collect their fruit. What impression do you get of them? Use quotations as evidence for your ideas.

_____

_____

_____

_____

_____

_____

_____

_____

_____

5 marks

6 The poet wrote this poem as an adult, looking back on a childhood memory. What impression does he give us of this memory?

_____

_____

_____

_____

_____

_____

_____

_____

_____

_____

5 marks

7

Read the extract and answer the questions that follow.

How to make the scrummiest pizza

You will need:
- Plain pizza bases – you can make these using the recipe on page 12 or buy them from the supermarket
- Tomato topping – see page 14 for our tasty topping
- Mozzarella – sliced
- Your fave toppings – slice these up and put them in bowls ready to use.

These are our fave toppings:
- Ham, mushroom and sweetcorn
- Pepperoni, green peppers, mushrooms and more pepperoni
- BBQ chicken (you can get this ready cooked from the supermarket), ham and pepper
- Cheese and tomato (sometimes simple is best!)
- Prawns and spinach (honestly!)
- Peppers, mushrooms and pineapple

How to do it:

1 First, take your pizza base and plaster it with the tomato topping. Don't let this go over the edge as it'll slide off and burn in the oven!

2 Next place slices of mozzarella on the tomato – it's up to you how much you like.

3 Now for the fun bit: carefully position your favourite toppings on your pizza. There are no rules but we've found it's best to have between 2 and 5 different toppings.

4 When you are happy with your creation, carefully put it in a hot oven (180–200°C) for 12–20 minutes, depending on the size of the pizza and the amount of topping you have. It's probably best to set the timer to check it after 10 minutes. It's also a good idea to ask an adult to help with this bit.

5 You'll know when it's ready to enjoy because the cheese will have melted and it'll look and smell mouth-watering! Take it out of the oven carefully (get someone to help with this), put it on a plate and enjoy!

Don't forget the boring washing-up bit – it's worth it if you want to use the kitchen again!

- Purpose = _____
- Audience = _____
- Text type = _____

Getting to grips with the text

1 Put numbers in the boxes to show the correct order to do these things:

Put the mozzarella on the pizza	☐	Put your favourite toppings on the pizza	☐
Make the tomato topping	☐	Put the pizza in the oven	☐

1 mark

2 Who is the intended audience of this text? Explain how you know.

_____

_____

_____

3 The language of this text helps to make it clear and easy to follow. Choose a word or phrase that is used to make it easy to follow and explain how it does this.

_____

_____

_____

4 This text uses informal language and phrases. Identify an informal word or phrase and explain why it has been used.

_____

_____

_____

5 In the list of 'our fave toppings' there are comments in brackets. Explain why it says '(sometimes simple is best!)' after 'Cheese and tomato'.

_____

_____

6 Do you think this text is likely to make young people want to make the pizza? You should comment on how the text:
- Makes the recipe seem fun
- Makes a connection with the reader
- Makes the recipe seem easy.

_____

_____

_____

_____

_____

_____

_____

_____

_____

_____

_____

8

Read the extract from *An Arrest*, by Ambrose Bierce, and answer the questions that follow on pages 22–23.

Having murdered his brother-in-law, Orrin Brower of Kentucky was a fugitive from justice. From the county jail where he had been confined to await his trial he had escaped by knocking down his jailer with an iron bar, robbing him of his keys and, opening the outer door, walking out into the night. The jailer being unarmed, Brower got no weapon with which to defend his recovered liberty. As soon as he was out of the town he had the folly to enter a forest; this was many years ago, when that region was wilder than it is now.

The night was pretty dark, with neither moon nor stars visible, and as Brower had never dwelt thereabout, and knew nothing of the lay of the land, he was, naturally, not long in losing himself. He could not have said if he were getting farther away from the town or going back to it – a most important matter to Orrin Brower. He knew that in either case a posse of citizens with a pack of bloodhounds would soon be on his track and his chance of escape was very slender; but he did not wish to assist in his own pursuit. Even an added hour of freedom was worth having.

Suddenly he emerged from the forest into an old road, and there before him saw, indistinctly, the figure of a man, motionless in the gloom. It was too late to retreat: the fugitive felt that at the first movement back toward the wood he would be, as he afterward explained, "filled with buckshot". So the two stood there like trees, Brower nearly suffocated by the activity of his own heart; the other – the emotions of the other are not recorded.

A moment later – it may have been an hour – the moon sailed into a patch of unclouded sky and the hunted man saw that visible embodiment of Law lift an arm and point significantly toward and beyond him. He understood. Turning his back to his captor, he walked submissively away in the direction indicated, looking to neither the right nor the left; hardly daring to breathe, his head and back actually aching with a prophecy of buckshot.

Brower was as courageous a criminal as ever lived to be hanged; that was shown by the conditions of awful personal peril in which he had coolly killed his brother-in-law. It is needless to relate them here; they came out at his trial, and the revelation of his calmness  in confronting them came near to saving his neck. But what would you have? – when a brave man is beaten, he submits.

So they pursued their journey jailward along the old road through the woods. Only once did Brower venture a turn of the head: just once, when he was in deep shadow and he knew that the other was in moonlight, he looked backward. His captor was Burton Duff, the jailer, as white as death and bearing upon his brow the livid mark of the iron bar. Orrin Brower had no further curiosity.

Eventually they entered the town, which was all alight, but deserted; only the women and children remained, and they were off the streets. Straight toward the jail the criminal held his way. Straight up to the main entrance he walked, laid his hand upon the knob of the heavy iron door, pushed it open without command, entered and found himself in the presence of a half-dozen armed men. Then he turned. Nobody else entered.

On a table in the corridor lay the dead body of Burton Duff.

• Purpose = _____

• Audience = _____

• Text type = _____

Getting to grips with the text

1 Why is Orrin Brower a 'fugitive from justice'?

_____

_____

1 mark

2 What is the name of the jailer?

_____

1 mark

3 The table gives examples of descriptive words and phrases used in the text.
Fill in the table to explain the impression each word or phrase gives.

Example of descriptive phrase	Impression it creates
'the moon sailed into a patch of unclouded sky'	The moon is free and moves easily. This contrasts with the actions of the fugitive.
'as white as death'	
'the livid mark of the iron bar'	

4 The first sentence of the story gives us lots of background information.

a Explain what it tells us.

_____

_____

2 marks

b Explain why it includes so much information in one sentence.

_____

_____

2 marks

5 The story includes hints that the man who is making Orrin return to the jail is a ghost. Identify one of these hints and explain why it is used.

_____

_____

_____

_____

2 marks

6 Look again at the last two paragraphs. How does the structure of the piece make the ending dramatic?

_____

_____

_____

_____

_____

_____

_____

_____

_____

_____

_____

_____

_____

_____

_____

_____

_____

9

Read the extract and answer the questions that follow.

★★★★★

Another cracking adventure with Wallace and Gromit

It's hard to believe it's been ten long years since Wallace last put the poor long-suffering Gromit through his paces, but now they're back, and with more gadgets than ever before! Yes, Wallace and Gromit hit the big screen, big time in a big full-length movie guaranteed to delight movie-goers of all ages.

From the moment the cheese-loving Wallace reappears on our screens, it's clear that Nick Park and his fellow animators haven't lost their touch, or their sense of humour. This film is not only a great story, but is also littered with jokes, from the 'Smug' fridge to the Austin Powers-type double entendres about melons.

The Plasticine models are a joy to see, full of fingerprints and energy in a way Computer Generated Imagery can never be. Furthermore, the voices are perfect for their characters; I even forgot superstars such as Helena Bonham-Carter and Ralph Fiennes were 'playing' Lady Tottington and Victor Quartermaine. Maybe that means they weren't really needed?

The plot isn't always as fast-moving as it could be, perhaps that's so they can make it the full-length film this is, but it's a hugely satisfying watch and justly deserving of its Oscar.

Getting to grips with the text

- Purpose = _____

- Audience = _____

- Text type = _____

1 This extract was written to review the film and express the reviewer's opinion. Explain why the stars have been put at the top of the review.

_____

1 mark

2 The review uses lots of adjectives. Identify a phrase using adjectives and explain what effect their use has.

_____

_____

_____

1 mark

3 What technique has the reviewer used here, and what impact does it have?

'Yes, Wallace and Gromit hit the big screen, big time in a big full-length movie guaranteed to delight movie-goers of all ages.'

_____

_____

_____

4 This is a review, so it is giving the writer's opinion. However, it does contain some facts. Identify a fact and explain why it has been used.

_____

_____

_____

5 The review uses a friendly and informal tone. Identify a word or phrase that is friendly and informal and explain why it has been used.

_____

_____

_____

6 The review ends with 'it's a hugely satisfying watch and justly deserving of its Oscar'. Explain how the whole of the review supports this opinion.

_____

_____

_____

_____

_____

_____

_____

_____

_____

_____

_____

_____

_____

_____

_____

10

Read the extract and answer the questions that follow.

BORDONDOWN SCHOOL
LONGFIELD ROAD
BATH

Dear Parent

Thank you for your interest in our school. I am pleased to enclose a school prospectus and invitation to our next open day.

As you know Bordondown is a thriving school where staff and students work hard for top results. We are lucky to have some very talented members of the school community and we are looking forward to another year of excellent examination results, with many of our students going on to Oxbridge and other top universities.

The focus of every school day is learning, and every activity is geared to support your child in their journey to become a successful learner; perhaps he or she will be one of our Oxbridge students of the future?

Learning is the key to a successful life, and we insist on discipline in order to achieve it. From correct uniform to homework being completed on time, we find an organised student is a successful student.

In addition to the timetabled day, there are many extra-curricular activities available for your child; a browse through the booklet in the prospectus will outline some of these.

Although the prospectus provides a comprehensive guide to our school, the best way to find out about its workings is to visit us. We would be delighted to show you round the school, provide students for you to talk to, and answer any questions you might have. These tours do get very busy, so please book a place by returning the form or telephoning the office.

I look forward to meeting you soon,

Yours faithfully,

Matthew Best

Head teacher

Oxbridge: Oxford and Cambridge Universities

- Purpose = _____

- Audience = _____

- Text type = _____

Getting to grips with the text

1 Why has the head teacher written this letter?

_____

1 mark

2 Mr Best writes about the success some students have had:
'many of our students going on to Oxbridge and other top universities.'
What does this suggest he regards as school success?

_____

_____

_____

2 marks

3 Although this letter is from one person, he uses the plural pronoun 'we'
throughout. Suggest why he does this and what impression he is trying
to give.

_____

_____

_____

2 marks

4 The letter uses very short paragraphs. Explain why.

_____

_____

1 mark

5 What impression of Bordondown School is created by this letter?

_____

_____

_____

_____

_____

_____

_____

_____

_____

_____

_____

_____

_____

_____

_____

5 marks

Practice reading paper

Try this practice reading paper.

Make sure you are in a quiet place and can spend 1 hour 15 minutes without being disturbed.

You are allowed 15 minutes reading time in the test, so set a timer or ask someone to tell you when the reading time is up.

- Spend 15 minutes reading pages 29–35 and highlighting or marking the purpose, audience and text type of each text. You might also like to mark any interesting style or language features.

- When the 15 minutes reading time is up, you can turn to the question paper. You have 1 hour to answer the questions.

- There are 14 questions about these texts and they are worth 32 marks in total.

- Remember to look at the marks available and make sure you provide enough information to get full marks.

Blood

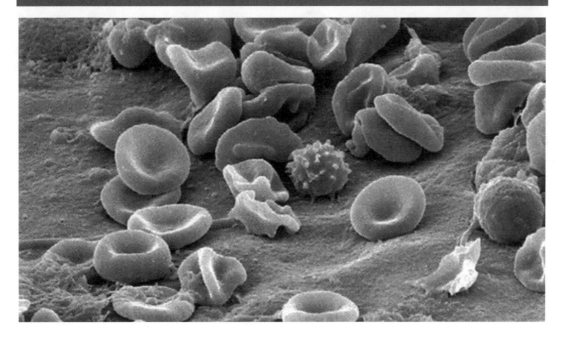

Contents	
Shades of red	pages 30–31
A recipe for blood	pages 32–33
A study in scarlet	pages 34–35

The texts in this booklet are all about blood. They explain the scientific facts about blood, and what it can tell us about people.

This is an extract from a booklet written for people who give blood. It gives information about the different colours blood can be and explains what this says about the donor.

Shades of red

What does the colour of your blood say about you?

Have you ever wondered why your blood seems to be a different shade of red from the donor on the next bed? Have you been concerned your blood looks more like Ribena than the finest Merlot? Although all blood is red, the shades vary between donors and can even be used to indicate health issues.

On average there are 35 trillion red blood cells, suspended in plasma, circulating in your body at any one time. Red cells are filled with haemoglobin that gives your blood its red colour.

Blood naturally changes colour during its journey around your body. When you take a breath, the inhaled oxygen in your lungs attaches itself to haemoglobin in the red cells. At this point your blood is oxygenated and a strong, bright poppy-red.

On their journey around your body, red cells exchange oxygen for carbon dioxide which returns to your lungs through your veins. The carbon dioxide is exhaled and the whole process begins again. At the end of the journey, your blood will appear a darker shade of red.

Blood is the transport system of your body. It not only carries energy to the cells but it also carries anything else that you ingest or absorb through your skin. Which also helps to explain

Our scientific staff have developed methods of visually checking the colour of your donation, as an additional safety measure. Much like a decorator's colour chart, donations are compared to a set of standard colour shades. Using colourmetric standards is another way we can help provide safer blood to the patient.

why not everyone's blood is the same shade.

Having bright red blood is not necessarily a sign of good health. Heavy smokers may produce a vividly coloured donation because carbon monoxide in cigarette smoke is attached much more easily to red cells than oxygen. The blood is bright red because of the presence of a cherry-red compound called carboxyhaemoglobin, which forms when carbon monoxide binds to haemoglobin.

If blood looks pinkish, it may be due to a high level of water insoluble fats, called lipaemia. Lipaemia can be inherited or caused by a fatty diet.

Wine buffs may like to know that claret-coloured blood suggests haemoglobin may be leaking from the red cells; a natural part of blood's ageing process called haemolysis.

Colour match

You might be surprised to know our staff back at the centres look out for darker donations because deep shades imply possible bacterial contamination or incorrect storage. They are also vigilant for blood which appears to be clumped or

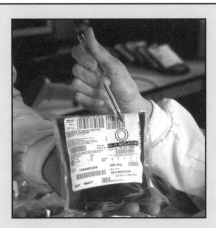

clotted or which looks darker in patches and may be unsuitable for transfusion.

The colour of plasma, which is usually straw-yellow, also varies enormously. Its colour can be seen after the blood has been separated, and the red cells removed. Some oral contraceptives turn plasma bright green and self-tanning pills may make it go a fluorescent orange!

Plasma is usually a clear yellow. However, it can look cloudy occasionally. This can be caused by a number of things. You could simply have eaten some fatty food before giving blood, or it could be caused by an underlying condition related to a high fat content in the body. It may even indicate a problem with the donation in relation to bacteria.

Our staff are trained to notice these differences and

act accordingly. In most cases colour and cloudiness are not a problem. But, in rare instances, it might mean referring the donor to their GP, or in the case of possible bacterial contamination, not using the donation, just to be on the safe side.

So, the next time you tuck into an oily curry the night before you donate, have a think about what colour your blood might be.

Did you know...

The importance of blood colour has endured through history, surviving in expressions we use today. The term 'blue-blooded', implying that someone is royal, was taken from the Spanish sangre azul and was adopted by the English in the 1830s. The English aristocracy spent little time outdoors in the sunlight and powdered and painted their skin white. Commoners believed that aristocrats had blue blood in their veins as this was how the veins appeared through such pale, translucent skin. Another well-known expression, 'red-blooded', now means 'vigorous' or 'virile' but may have originated from male warriors returning from battle and being bloodied.

Merlot and **claret** are both types of red wine.

This is an extract from a GCSE Science textbook. It explains about the chemical properties of blood.

A recipe for blood

On average a human adult has about five litres of blood inside them. About 40% of blood is made up of blood cells. There are three kinds of blood cell.

Red blood cells

There are 25 million million of these in an adult's body. They contain the red pigment haemoglobin and their main function is to carry oxygen from the lungs to the cells of the body. These cells live for about four months and are continually replaced.

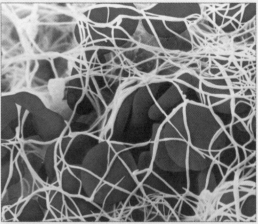

Red blood cells in a blood clot. The white material is strands of fibrin – the basis of the clot.

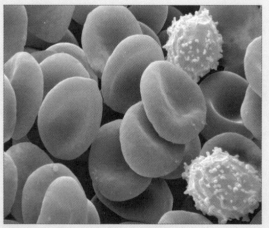

Two white blood cells in a sea of red blood cells. You can clearly see their different structure and shape.

White blood cells

These are the cells of defence and are fewer in number than red blood cells. There are two types: the phagocytes which eat disease organisms (microbes) and the lymphocytes which produce antibodies that act like chemical missiles against disease.

Platelets

These are tiny bodies in the blood that help to clot the blood. If the skin is damaged or cut this can let microbes in, so an emergency repair system quickly comes into action. Once a blood vessel is damaged the blood starts to leak out. When platelets come into contact with the air they break open. This causes a chain of reactions involving other chemicals in the blood (blood proteins) that leads to a clot forming in the damaged area.

Plasma

The other 60% of blood is a fluid called **plasma**. This is an almost colourless liquid (slightly yellow) that contains an enormous amount of substances such as:

- Water

- Dissolved food (glucose, amino acids, fats)

- Waste products (carbon dioxide, urea)

- Minerals

- Antibodies

- Blood clotting proteins

- Hormones

The bone marrow produces about 200 000 million red blood cells each day. Before a red blood cell dies it will have made about 172 000 journeys around the body. The blood vessels of the average adult would stretch almost $2\frac{1}{2}$ times around the Earth (about 95 000 km) if they were unravelled.

pigment = colouring

This is an extract from the first Sherlock Holmes novel, *A study in scarlet*, by Sir Arthur Conan Doyle. It was first published in 1887 and is narrated by Dr. Watson. This is the first time Dr. Watson has met Holmes, and they are introduced by Mr. Stamford.

This was a lofty chamber, lined and littered with countless bottles. Broad, low tables were scattered about, which bristled with retorts, test-tubes, and little Bunsen lamps, with their blue flickering flames. There was only one student in the room, who was bending over a distant table absorbed in his work. At the sound of our steps he glanced round and sprang to his feet with a cry of pleasure. "I've found it! I've found it," he shouted to my companion, running towards us with a test-tube in his hand. "I have found a re-agent which is precipitated by haemoglobin, and by nothing else." Had he discovered a gold mine, greater delight could not have shone upon his features.

"Dr. Watson, Mr. Sherlock Holmes," said Stamford, introducing us.

"How are you?" he said cordially, gripping my hand with a strength for which I should hardly have given him credit. "You have been in Afghanistan, I perceive."

"How on earth did you know that?" I asked in astonishment.

"Never mind," said he, chuckling to himself. "The question now is about haemoglobin. No doubt you see the significance of this discovery of mine?"

"It is interesting, chemically, no doubt," I answered, "but practically …"

"Why, man, it is the most practical medico-legal discovery for years. Don't you see that it gives us an infallible test for blood stains. Come over here now!" He seized me by the coat-sleeve in his eagerness, and drew me over to the table at which he had been working. "Let us have some fresh blood," he said, digging a long bodkin into his finger, and drawing off the resulting drop of blood in a chemical pipette. "Now, I add this small quantity of blood to a litre of water. You perceive that the resulting mixture has the appearance of pure water. The proportion of blood cannot be more than one in a million. I have no doubt, however, that we shall be able to obtain the characteristic reaction." As he spoke, he threw into the vessel a few white crystals, and then added some drops of a transparent fluid. In an instant the contents assumed a dull mahogany colour, and a brownish dust was precipitated to the bottom of the glass jar.

"Ha! ha!" he cried, clapping his hands, and looking as delighted as a child with a new toy. "What do you think of that?"

"It seems to be a very delicate test," I remarked.

"Beautiful! beautiful! The old Guiacum test was very clumsy and uncertain. So is the microscopic examination for blood corpuscles. The latter is valueless if the stains are a few hours old. Now, this appears to act as well whether the blood is old or new. Had this test been invented, there are hundreds of men now walking the earth who would long ago have paid the penalty of their crimes."

"Indeed!" I murmured.

"Criminal cases are continually hingeing upon that one point. A man is suspected of a crime months perhaps after it has been committed. His linen or clothes are examined, and brownish stains discovered upon them. Are they blood stains, or mud stains, or rust stains, or fruit stains, or what are they? That is a question which has puzzled many an expert, and why? Because there was no reliable test. Now we have the Sherlock Holmes' test, and there will no longer be any difficulty."

medico-legal = a combination of medical and legal evidence that can be used in law

infallible = something that cannot fail or be wrong

bodkin = a sharp instrument, a bit like a long pin

corpuscles = blood cells

1 In the section headed **Colour match**, why do staff at the National Blood Service centres look out for darker donations?

_____

_____

(1 mark)

2 Look again at the first paragraph, in the box. Explain why this has been placed at the beginning of the article.

_____

_____

_____

_____

_____

_____

_____

_____

(2 marks)

3 Look again at the information in the box. Why are the staff described as 'scientific'?

_____

_____

(1 mark)

4 This article also explains what can be learned from the colour of plasma:

Plasma is usually a clear yellow. However, it can look cloudy occasionally. This can be caused by a number of things. You could simply have eaten some fatty food before giving blood, or it could be caused by an underlying condition related to high fat content in the body. It may even indicate a problem with the donation with regard to bacteria.

    a How does the writer show that you cannot draw a direct conclusion from the colour of plasma?

_____

_____

_____

(2 marks)

b Why has the writer done this?

_____

_____

(1 mark)

5 The article is taken from a booklet sent to people registered as blood donors.
Why was the article included in the booklet?
You should comment on:
• The subject matter of the article
• The way it has been written
• The presentation and layout

_____

_____

_____

_____

_____

_____

_____

_____

_____

_____

_____

_____

_____

_____

_____

_____

_____

_____

_____

_____

_____

_____

(5 marks)

Questions 6–10 are about *A recipe for blood* (pages 32–33).

6 Why are platelets so important?

_____

(1 mark)

7 The information on these pages is intended to help GCSE students learn about Biology.
    a Explain why each paragraph is given a heading and how this helps the reader of the textbook.

_____

_____

(1 mark)

    b Explain why bullet points are used in the section headed **Plasma**, and how this helps the reader of the textbook.

_____

_____

(1 mark)

8 The writer has used brackets several times in this extract.
    a Identify and write down an example of brackets being used.

_____

(1 mark)

    b Explain why brackets are used in this way.

_____

_____

_____

(1 mark)

9 Why has this text been written? What is the writer trying to do?

_____

_____

_____

(1 mark)

10 How does the extract make this topic easy for the reader to follow?
You should comment on how the extract:
- Uses structural and layout devices
- Makes use of technical language and numbers
- Uses sentence structures.

(5 marks)

Questions 11–14 are about *A study in scarlet*, by Sir Arthur Conan Doyle (pages 34–35).

11 What does Watson think of Holmes? Use a quotation to support your answer.

_____

_____

_____

_____ (2 marks)

12 Why does Holmes think his discovery is so important?

_____

_____

_____ (1 mark)

13 'This was a lofty chamber, lined and littered with countless bottles.'
What does the choice of language suggest about the room in which Holmes is working?

_____

_____

_____

_____ (2 marks)

14 What impression of Sherlock Holmes do you get from this extract?

_____

_____

_____

_____

_____

_____

_____

_____

_____

_____

_____

_____

_____

_____

_____

_____

_____

_____

_____

_____

_____

_____

_____

_____

_____

_____

_____

_____

(5 marks)

The writing paper

The key things you need to know

This Workbook contains exercises and practice writing tasks for you to work through at your own pace. You will need to use separate paper to answer the writing tasks. If you want to check your own answers, you will find instructions on the inside back cover.

When you've worked through the practice tasks, have a go at the mock test paper. Try to do this in proper test conditions, spending 1 hour and 15 minutes on it. You will need someone to time you. Spend 45 minutes on the longer writing task (worth 30 marks) and 30 minutes on the shorter writing task (worth 20 marks).

The tasks

This Workbook contains different questions to help you prepare for what comes up in the real test. When you read each question, the first thing you need to decide is:
• the **audience** you need to write for
• the **purpose** of your writing
• the **text type** you have been asked to write in.
The questions give you this information, so make sure you use it in your planning.

Each task is linked to one of the **writing triplets** from the National Curriculum:
• inform, explain, describe
• imagine, explore, entertain
• analyse, review, comment
• persuade, argue, advise.

The questions

There are longer and shorter writing tasks. You are provided with a planning page for the longer task – make sure you use it, as it will help you structure your answer effectively. There is no planning page for the shorter task – you are expected to plan for yourself in this task.

The longer tasks test Writing Assessment Focuses (AF) 1–7 and the shorter tasks test Assessment Focuses 1–2 and 4–8; just as they will in the real thing you'll sit in May:

AF1: write imaginative, interesting and thoughtful tasks
This means your work is interesting to read and shows your ideas.

AF2: produce texts which are appropriate to task, reader and purpose
This means your work is suitable for the intended audience, purpose and text type.

AF3: organise and present whole texts effectively, sequencing and structuring information, ideas and events
This means your ideas are easy to follow and develop in a logical way.

AF4: construct paragraphs and use cohesion within and between paragraphs
This means you use paragraphs and it is easy for the reader to see how each paragraph leads on to the next one. It is only assessed in the longer writing task.

AF5: vary sentences for clarity, purpose and effect
This means you construct your sentences to help convey your ideas. For example, you might use a very short simple sentence after a build-up of complex sentences to create contrast and impact.

AF6: write with technical accuracy of syntax and punctuation in phrases, clauses and sentences
Your word order is correct and your sentences say exactly what you want them to.

AF7: select appropriate and effective vocabulary
This means you choose carefully the best words for your writing.

AF8: use correct spelling
This is only assessed in the shorter writing task.

Answering the questions

- You should start by reading the question really carefully and identifying **purpose**, **audience** and **text type**.

- Then get your ideas into a plan. This will help to shape your writing.

- Once you know what you are going to write about, and the order you are going to put your ideas in, you can start writing.

Timing the test paper

- Spend 45 minutes on the longer writing task and 30 minutes on the shorter writing task, including planning time. Make sure you leave time at the end to go through and check, correct and improve what you have written.

Planning your answer

The writing questions all follow the same sort of format:

Arts for all ← The title of the task – this doesn't have to be the title you use.

You are employed by a local theatre to organise an arts festival every year.

You are about to plan this year's festival so decide to look at some feedback forms from last year's event.

The role you need to adopt. This will affect the tone of your writing. It also gives you an idea about the purpose and audience.

Arts Festival
- There were lots of great activities for the 3–7 age range.
- You needed to provide more cleaning facilities, my kids got paint all over the car on the journey home.
- The festival is just for kids but adults need art too!
- The end of festival exhibition and production was fantastic. What a sense of achievement.

Scene setting – ideas to get you thinking. You can add your own ideas to the ones you are given.

Write a report for your team to explain your plans for this year's festival.

Your actual task. It tells you purpose, audience and text type. In this case that's:
Purpose: to explain
Audience: your team at the theatre
Text type: a report

(30 marks)

Purpose, audience and text type

1 Read these text extracts and match each one to its intended audience and purpose (see opposite).

---

1 I wish to highlight the appalling state of the roads in my town. There are huge potholes which are not only uncomfortable but dangerous to all road users. Yesterday, I saw a cyclist fall off his bike after his front wheel went down one of these traps. Action is needed …

---

2 Good morning.

I would like to speak to you this morning about our need for proper cycle paths to school. We all know that cycling to school is fast and healthy, but only if we are not in danger from lorries and cars thundering past, threatening to knock us over.

Cycle paths could be our safe route to school, but we need to fight for them and that's where you come in …

---

3 Secondly, if the school were to provide safer cycle sheds more students would cycle to school, which would reduce the traffic around the school and make the roads safer for everyone. This is a benefit the school cannot ignore as it would also have a positive environmental impact …

---

4 Thank you for your interest in our Premium Cycle Sheds. I enclose a comprehensive brochure detailing the different models and options available and would like to draw your attention to the following points that make our product the market-leader:
• Value for money
• Designed to fit your school's needs
• Sturdy and secure
• Long-lasting and guaranteed for ten years

Our customers often find the best way to make a decision is with the help of one of our experts, and I am pleased to confirm that Lilly George will be happy to come and visit you to explain your options …

---

5 <u>Issues with the Premium Cycle Shed</u>

Claims on the ten year guarantee are high, with specific problems related to rust and corrosion. The cost to upgrade the materials to prevent this problem is roughly equal to the cost of repairs following claims. However, the increased product confidence and potential sales implication would make this route valuable.

<u>Proposal</u>

Upgrade materials ….

Intended audience

a Your head teacher
b Potential customer
c Your whole year group
d Project manager
e Local council members

Purpose (you might find the texts have more than one purpose)

i Persuade, argue, advise
ii Inform, explain, describe
iii Imagine, explore, entertain
iv Analyse, review, comment

Text	Intended audience	Purpose
1		
2		
3		
4		
5		

2 There are problems with these cycle sheds. Imagine you are the head teacher and you are not happy with the Premium Cycle Sheds you purchased for your school last year.

On a separate sheet of paper, write your letter of complaint to the company.

3 Now try identifying the **purpose, audience** and **text type** in this task.

Local radio star

You work as a radio presenter for your local radio station. You are going to the monthly meeting to suggest new ideas to make the radio station more interesting for young people in your area.

Your research has found the following:

Local radio for local teens

- Include information about local events for teenagers
- Have local teenage voices presenting – we don't want an adult telling us what to think
- Don't be afraid to raise difficult issues
- A good mix of new music, perhaps from local bands
- A review of gadgets and new stuff

Write a report to advise the radio station controller what to include in the new programme for teenagers.

Purpose _____

Audience _____

Text type _____

Using the right words

1 Amazing adjectives

Look at these adjectives. They can all be used to describe your tests.
Sort them into the correct column in the table.

> stimulating   boring   tedious   essential   exciting   challenging
> interesting   mundane   ordinary   dull   normal   wearisome
> vital   crucial   monotonous   necessary   commonplace   usual

negative	neutral	positive
dull		

2 Vary your verbs

How many other words can you think of to replace these verbs?

a go _____

b said _____

c sleep _____

d cry _____

e walk _____

3 Use Standard English

How would you change these if you were giving a formal presentation?

a This product is really *cool*. _____

b I'll *catch* you later. _____

c I *dunno* what to suggest. _____

d *Hi ya!* _____

e We don't want to be *ripped off*. _____

4 Add some pictures

Can you think of any similes you can use to describe the following?

a a really fierce deputy head teacher _____

b a jolly and cheerful footballer _____

c a huge grey factory _____

d a small boat out at sea _____

e a child skiing down a mountain _____

5 Tug at the heart-strings

Can you change these phrases to make them more emotive?

a Young man hits old woman.

_____

b The Guildford Flames beat their opposition.

_____

c When the sun is shining I enjoy a cold drink.

_____

d We have to stay inside the house because there is too much snow around.

_____

e The old cat tried to catch a bird and failed.

_____

6 Know when to avoid bias

Can you change these emotive phrases into neutral ones?

a The bear ripped him to shreds.

_____

b The woodland was ravished by a terrifying blaze.

_____

c He shovelled the greasy burger into his mouth as if he was starved.

_____

d She shrieked as the thug yanked the handbag from her arm.

_____

e The crumbling school buildings are a death-trap.

_____

Sentence structures

1 Add some complexity

Re-write these extracts, changing the sentence structure to make them more powerful and coherent.

a I am very excited. I am going on holiday to America tomorrow. My whole family are going. What's really good is that I am allowed to take my best friend.

_____

_____

_____

b Cats are natural predators. When they see a bird or mouse it just means excitement to them. Sometimes they kill without the desire to eat their prey. Some cats can be shocked when they catch something.

_____

_____

_____

_____

2 Watch the length

These sentences are out of control. Re-write them, putting in punctuation to make the meaning clearer.

a The market was full of exciting smells and colours and noises and people and new things.

_____

_____

b Music can create the atmosphere you need to learn and it can even help you to remember ideas because when you come to revise you can listen to the same music and it will help you to recall the original idea because your memory has made a link.

_____

_____

_____

_____

_____

_____

_____

3 Zoom into the action

Look at this sentence:

> In the shadows, under the stairs, resting against the chair was a bloody knife.

The reader is taken closer and closer to the really important discovery of the knife by the phrases that start the sentence.

Complete these sentences to zoom your reader into the action!

a At the end of the garden, beyond the tree was _____ .

b In the car, sitting quietly as directed, _____ .

c In the corner of the room, _____

_____ .

d Under the floorboards, _____

_____ .

4 Add layers of meaning

A complex sentence has a main clause and one or more subordinate clauses:

> They ate chocolates greedily, until they felt sick.

The main clause, 'They ate chocolates greedily' can be understood by itself but the subordinate clause, 'until they felt sick' doesn't make sense by itself.

Underline the main clause in red and the subordinate clause in blue, in these sentences.

a I hid under the duvet shaking, as the storm raged outside.

b Claire, who was filled with a sense of relief, left the stage.

c Until the power cut hit, Paul refused to leave his computer.

Re-write these as complex sentences. You might choose to put the subordinate clause at the beginning, in the middle or at the end.

d Sally loved the book. She missed her bus because she was reading it. _____

_____

e The computer finally died. It had been used non-stop. _____

_____

f Amanda bought some new pink shoes. She loved shopping. _____

_____

Paragraphs and structure

1 Read this extract and mark where the paragraphs should go. You might want to change the order.

When you first see my house you might think it's a bit dull and dingy because there are plants growing up the front wall and the path is a bit overgrown. I like to think this adds character and makes it more exciting when you come and visit me. If I trust you, and the others say it's OK, I might take you to the end of the garden to see our den. It's taken us years to create it and it's simply the best place to be in the summer. Once you are in you'll probably be drawn into the kitchen as there's generally something good cooking and that's where we tend to be. It's funny really, as it's the smallest room in the house but it's where we spend our time together. (Well, not the smallest, but you wouldn't all sit round the bathroom to talk about the day, would you?) Stepping through the front door for the first time is normally a bit of a shock because we've painted the inside really bright colours. The woodwork (that's the doors and skirting boards) is pink and the walls are purple. My gran hates it, but we sat down and made a family decision so it's fine by us.

2 You also need to start new paragraphs when there's a new speaker. Mark the paragraph breaks in this extract with a forward slash (/).

"Look, I'm really sorry," said Barry with frustration, "but this is just not going to work and that's an end to it." He threw down the play script and stood up to go. Laura looked up at him. "I'm really sorry as well," she said with sarcasm, "I'm really sorry that we've wasted so much time rehearsing with you in the lead role when we could have had Lance. He would at least have listened to our ideas." "That's just typical, " replied Barry, "and that's why I'm leaving. You've never wanted me in this stupid play. Well, if you think Lance will have anything to do with you when he hears how you've treated me you've got another think coming!" The rest of the cast sat watching with amazement as he coolly collected his jacket and walked out of the rehearsal room. Laura sat stunned. "Did that really just happen?" she asked, "Did we finally get rid of that idiot?" "Yes!" shouted Sian with joy. "Well done, you finally did it!"

3 Choose the appropriate connectives from the list and add them to the recipe below.

| Next | Finally | Then | Secondly | Firstly |

_____ pre-heat the oven to 180°.

_____ take your vegetables and chop them into 1 cm size cubes.

_____ lightly oil the baking tray and arrange the vegetables on it so they are evenly spaced.

_____ put the tray in the oven and set the timer to 40 minutes.

_____ remove the vegetables from the oven and enjoy!

Writing in different formats

1 Look at the text types in the box and the list of writing elements below. Match the most likely text type (or types) to each element.

> letter   newspaper   story   leaflet   report   speech

- Your address in the top right

  _____

- Impersonal phrases

  _____

- The date

  _____

- Snappy headline

  _____

- Alliteration

  _____

- Short paragraphs

  _____

- Bullet points

  _____

- Sign-off of 'Yours faithfully, Yours sincerely' or a more informal phrase if you know the person

  _____

- Rhetorical techniques

  _____

- Entertain and inform

  _____

- Informal style

  _____

- Repetition

  _____

- Clear but lively

  _____

- Factual

  _____

- Formal address

  _____

- Short sentences

  _____

- Clear statement of purpose

  _____

- Sub-heading

  _____

- Modal verbs

  _____

- Emotive language

  _____

- Personal pronouns

  _____

- The address of the person you are writing to in the top left

  _____

- Formal style

  _____

- Quotations from experts

  _____

- Pattern of three

  _____

- Varied length of sentences

  _____

2 Label these features in the newspaper article below.

> headline   sub-heading   use of expert   illustration   caption

PET FISH FRIED
Fish lover left red-faced

Paul Roberts, fish owning expert, was left red-faced yesterday, after he managed to fry hundreds of pounds worth of Koi Carp.

Roberts, who travels the world advising on the care of these creatures, fitted his own water filter system, something he advises his readers to leave to the professionals.

Unfortunately, he made a fatal error with the wiring and managed to heat his pond to near-tropical temperatures! The poor fish didn't stand a chance, as their home boiled and then exploded.

The stone pond exploded under the pressure of the boiling water and the boiled carp were sent flying. "My cat thought it was wonderful as cooked fish came flying through the air" explained Roberts' neighbour, Brian Downing, "although it was a horrendous noise!"

Roberts wasn't available for comment, but his wife said he was shocked and very saddened.

£400 Koi cat food

3 Now find these features in the speech below.

> emotive language   repetition   alliteration   list of three

" Everybody knows that litter is dirty and dangerous. So why do we just drop our litter?

Rats are attracted to places with lots of litter, such as our school. Now, you might have an idea of rats as cute and cuddly, but they actually spread dangerous diseases such as cholera, typhus and leptospirosis. We do not want these around our school, so why do we just drop our litter?

We need to make a stand. We need to make a difference. You need to make a difference.

Firstly, take responsibility for your own actions. Put your litter in a bin or your bag.

Secondly, take responsibility for our community. Challenge anyone you see dropping litter. Explain what the consequences could be and ask them to put their litter in a bin.

Finally, if you see a piece of litter, don't walk over it: deal with it. By doing this you will make a difference. "

Punctuation

1 Write these sentences correctly.

a i am going to the shop to buy some crisps my dog needs to walk

_____

_____

b the shopping centre banned teenagers as they were bad news they thought

_____

_____

c james and amanda are going to france to learn to ski i hope they enjoy it

_____

_____

d i can't believe top of the pops is still going after all these years it's really amazing

_____

_____

e my english teacher is going to be really impressed with my improved writing skills

_____

_____

2 Use commas, dashes, colons, semi-colons and brackets to improve these sentences.

a You will need a pen a pencil and a ruler.

_____

b I had a great birthday thanks.

_____

c Jane likes Shakespeare Caroline prefers modern drama.

_____

d The bread which was actually put out for the birds had been eaten by the cat.

_____

_____

3 Shorten these words using an apostrophe.

    a I am   _____

    b it is   _____

    c they are   _____

    d you are   _____

    e we are   _____

4 Remove the apostrophe from these words and write them out in full.

    a he's   _____

    b let's   _____

    c could've   _____

    d can't   _____

    e we've   _____

5 Re-write these sentences using an apostrophe to show ownership.

    a The cats which belonged to Lucy were hungry.

    _____

    b Let's all go round to the flat belonging to Wayne for a party.

    _____

    c I won all the prizes at the sports day belonging to my school.

    _____

    d The provision for young people provided by my town is inadequate.

    _____

    e The car belonging to my brother is a heap of junk.

    _____

Spelling

1 Plurals
Change these words into plurals.

a bus   _buses_

b try   _____

c potato   _____

d church   _____

e child   _____

f sheep   _____

g fox   _____

h car   _____

i tomato   _____

j business   _____

k calf   _____

l rush   _____

2 Present to past
Write the present participle and past tense of these verbs.

a to run   _running_   _ran_

b to stop   _____   _____

c to drop   _____   _____

d to decide   _____   _____

e to watch   _____   _____

f to form   _____   _____

g to admit   _____   _____

h to prefer   _____   _____

i to benefit   _____   _____

j to state   _____   _____

k to fight   _____   _____

l to begin   _____   _____

3 Misspellings

Write these words correctly.

a acomodation _____

b asessment _____

c audince _____

d buisness _____

e embarase _____

f explaination _____

g intresting _____

h marrage _____

i peple _____

j recieve _____

k secondery _____

l seperate _____

m sincerly _____

n serprise _____

o tommorow _____

p wierd _____

4 Beware of homophones

Underline the correct word in these sentences.

a Lance and Susan are looking forward to **they're / there / their** holiday.

b "**Who's / Whose** homework is this?" asked the teacher. "It doesn't have a name!"

c The old house was very creepy at night because it was so **quiet / quite**.

d "You may all go to lunch **accept / except** Katie."

e You need to explain the **effect / affect** of the metaphor.

f Oh, look! My pen is over **they're / there / their**.

g "**Who's / Whose** up for swimming?" asked Andrea.

h I was **quiet / quite** pleased with my homework but the teacher didn't seem impressed.

i I've got to go up in assembly to **accept / except** a prize on behalf of my tutor group.

Writing to review: shorter writing task

Poor Luke!

You receive the following email from a friend who is recovering in hospital following an operation.

New Message

Send | New | Attach | Find | Font | Print

To:

Subject:

Hello there, thanks for your last email. I think I would die of boredom without your emails. I can't believe I'm only allowed to use the computer for half an hour a day! Oh well, got to share it, I suppose.

I'm having to spend time reading now, and I'm really getting into it. Have you read any good books or seen any good films lately? I'd love to hear about something you think I should read or watch.

Right, got to go now. I look forward to hearing from you!

All the best

Luke

> Don't forget you have to use Standard English, even though this is an email to a friend.

Write an email to Luke in which you review a book or film you think he will enjoy.

(20 marks including 4 marks for spelling)

> You are not provided with a planning sheet for the shorter writing task but you still need to plan!

Writing to comment: shorter writing task

Be the spokesperson!

Your school has conducted a survey to see if its students want to keep or change their school uniform.

Here are the results:

17% of students don't want any kind of uniform.

20% of students want to keep the current uniform.

63% of students want to keep a uniform, but not the current one.

– Of these, the majority want a more varied uniform.

– There is also much support for the idea that Years 10 and 11 have a slightly different uniform from Years 7–9.

The sixth form don't want a uniform at all.

The head teacher would like you to comment on these results so that the Leadership Team know what action to take.

Write your commentary on these results.

(20 marks including 4 marks for spelling)

You are not provided with a planning sheet for the shorter writing task but you still need to plan!

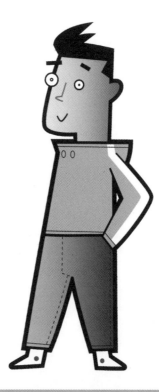

Writing to describe: shorter writing task

Celebrating past lives

Older people can be inspiring, interesting, scary or a mixture of all these things.

- • What have they seen/experienced?
- • How has this affected them today?
- • What do you think about them?

Think about an old person you know or have heard about, and write a detailed description of them.

(20 marks including 4 marks for spelling)

You are not provided with a planning sheet for the shorter writing task but you still need to plan!

Writing to explain: shorter writing task

Holiday decisions

Your family is trying to decide where to go on holiday.
You have found the following holiday:

> ## Family favourite
> Join us at Glowing Sands for the family holiday of a
> lifetime. There's so much to do, for all the family:
> - **Relaxation zone** – calm and tranquil, for those chill-out
>   times
> - **Music zone** – live music, karaoke and the club. Music
>   and performance lessons are available; who knows,
>   maybe you'll be on the stage at the end of the week?
> - **Art zone** – think, look, create. Express the artist in you.
> - **Beauty zone** – pamper your body and make sure it's a
>   whole new you at the end of the week.
> - **Nature zone** – for those who like to get out and about –
>   the beauty of our natural setting awaits. From nature
>   walks, to getting to grips with your gardening.
> - **Sea zone** – develop your skills on the sea. Windsurfing,
>   sailing and diving are all available.

Decide if you would like to go on this holiday or not.

Write your ideas down to explain them.

(20 marks including 4 marks for spelling)

> You are not provided
> with a planning sheet
> for the shorter writing
> task but you still need
> to plan!

Writing fiction: Longer writing task

New worlds, new experiences

You are writing a story about the first landing on a new planet.

Your characters have been travelling in space for over a year and have finally landed on this new planet.

Below are some notes you have made for the next chapter of this novel.

Notes for chapter about landing on Planet X

Include:

- How the characters feel after travelling for over a year
- Worries and concerns they have about what is about to happen
- Their first reaction to Planet X

Character notes:

- Ann is a 'get up and go' sort of person. She has found the journey really difficult.
- Afsheen is impatient to explore Planet X.
- Mark is very aware of the possible dangers of a new planet.

Write the next chapter of the novel.

(30 marks)

You may wish to use this page to plan your work.

(This page will not be marked.)

Don't forget to identify purpose, audience, text type!

- Notes about the journey and how the astronauts feel

- The conversation they have and the decisions they make before getting out

- The new planet – what they can see, hear, smell, taste, touch

- What happens when they get out of the spacecraft

Use lined paper to write your answer. You can assess your answer by following the guidance online at www.collinseducation.com/easylearning.

Writing to describe: Longer writing task

Local descriptions of local places

Your English teacher gives you the following and suggests you take part:

Local writers wanted to describe local places
WE NEED YOU!

We're publishing a new guide to the UK, but this time the entries are to be by people who really know their places. Rather than sending travel writers to visit your town for half a day and then write about it, we want to get the truth.

Write an entry for our new guidebook and you could see your work in our new book!

You will need to cover the following areas, but we want your description to be as interesting as possible:

• The setting and atmosphere

• Local life – what's going on there?

• The best bits

• Things that need to be changed

• Your overall impression.

Write a description of the place where you live, to enter the competition.

(30 marks)

You may wish to use this page to plan your work.

(This page will not be marked.)

Don't forget to identify purpose, audience, text type!

• What does it look like, what can you see? What is the atmosphere like?

• Local events – what is there to do?

• The good things about living here

• The bad things about living here

• What I think of the place where I live.

Use lined paper to write your answer. You can assess your answer by following the guidance online at www.collinseducation.com/easylearning.

Writing to inform: Longer writing task

The next stages of my life ...

You have received a letter from a relative you don't see very often. Here is part of it:

> I enjoyed reading about your school play and am sorry I wasn't able to come and see you. I am really pleased it went so well.
>
> I do enjoy reading about your school life. I know it must be boring for you to have to write about it, but school seems so different from when I was there (I don't want to admit how many years ago that was). What else is happening there?

Write a letter to this relative telling them about your school life.
Do not include an address.

You might like to use one or more of the following ideas:

• Your option choices for Year 10

• Your extra-curricular activities

• Your lessons

• How your school day is organised

(30 marks)

You may wish to use this page to plan your work.

(This page will not be marked.)

Don't forget to identify purpose, audience, text type!

- Ideas to open the letter and my response to the letter I was sent

Ideas to include in reply		
• The decisions I've had to make about my options	• The decisions I made and my reasons	• The events and changes I'm looking forward to

Use lined paper to write your answer. You can assess your answer by following the guidance online at www.collinseducation.com/easylearning.

Writing to review: Longer writing task

Music with you all day long ...

You work for a magazine that reviews electrical gadgets. You have been sent a new revolutionary music player to review. Here are the specifications:

MusicWrap

At last, a music player that doesn't need wires!

Key specifications:

- It looks like a wristwatch and tells the time, but it also plays music!
- You can download up to 10,000 tracks onto it.
- The music quality is second to none.
- It's wrapped round your wrist so you won't lose it!
- You don't need wires! Wireless technology means you just clip the headphones to your ears.
- Easy to use, fabulous to listen to!

Write the review for your magazine.

(30 marks)

You may wish to use this page to plan your work.

(This page will not be marked.)

Don't forget to identify purpose, audience, text type!

- What do you think of the idea?

- How does the wristwatch player work? Benefits? Problems?

- How do the wireless headphones work? Benefits? Problems?

- Would you recommend it?

Use lined paper to write your answer. You can assess your answer by following the guidance online at www.collinseducation.com/easylearning.

Supermarket threat

You read this article in your local paper:

Skate threat from supermarket

Local planning officers were considering a planning application from a large supermarket yesterday. Foods 'R'Us has applied to build a new store where the skatepark currently is.

Although the store will provide lots of jobs and be very useful for local people there is already some opposition to it.

Local shopkeepers are worried their small shops will go out of business and local kids want to know where they are supposed to go if their skatepark disappears.

Planning officers have raised these issues with Foods 'R'Us and are awaiting their reply. In the meantime, they have asked local people to let them know what they think. Write to …

Write a letter to the planning officer to advise them what to do.

Do not include an address.

(30 marks)

You may wish to use this page to plan your work.

(This page will not be marked.)

Advantages of the new supermarket being built	Disadvantages of the new supermarket being built
• More convenient shopping	• Loss of the skatepark
• More jobs	• Loss of local businesses

Use lined paper to write your answer. You can assess your answer by following the guidance online at www.collinseducation.com/easylearning.

Practice writing paper

Have a go at answering this practice writing paper.

Make sure you are in a quiet place and can spend 1 hour 15 minutes without being disturbed.

You need to keep an eye on the time so that you spend 45 minutes on the longer writing task and 30 minutes on the shorter writing task.

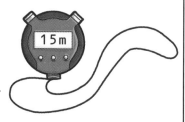

- Spend 15 minutes reading and planning the longer writing task. You are given a planning sheet. Although you don't *have* to use it, it does make sense to do so.

- Spend 25 minutes writing your answer to the longer writing task. This leaves you 5 minutes to go through checking, correcting and improving your work.

- Spend 10 minutes reading and planning the shorter writing task. Although you are not given a planning sheet, you still need to make a plan.

- Remember to spend 5 minutes going through and checking, correcting and improving your answer to this task.

Writing paper

Longer writing task

This is worth 30 marks and you should spend 45 minutes on it.

Shorter writing task

This is worth 20 marks, including 4 marks for spelling. You should spend 30 minutes on it.

You will need separate paper to answer these tasks. (in the actual test you'll be given an answer booklet).

Section A

Longer writing task

Money matters

You have just received the following information from the school governors:

The governors are delighted to announce that Liz Day, a past student, has made a gift of £10,000 to the school.

The governors would like to know what you, the students, think this money should be spent on. Some suggestions are listed below, or you can make your own suggestion:

• Use the money to buy new computer equipment.

• Buy new books for the library.

• Spend it on a school visit for the whole school.

• Build a statue of Miss Day to express thanks.

• Develop the school's sports facilities.

• Buy new musical instruments.

Write a letter to the governors to persuade them to spend the money on the project of your choice.

(30 marks)

Longer writing task

Planning page

You can use this page to make notes for your letter.

(This page will not be marked.)

- What should the money be spent on?

- Why is this a good project?

- Why is this better than other ideas?

- How will it benefit the whole school?

Shorter writing task

Teen TV

You receive a memo from your boss:

> I've just received this data from our research team. It looks like we need a new programme for teenagers – to fill the 4–4.30 slot.
>
> Have a look at the data and let me have your ideas as quickly as possible, please.

Research into new teenage show:

We need something new for 4–4.30.

- This is prime time for the teen market – they are home and could be in front of the TV.

- There was a positive response to the following content:
  - Live music
  - Magazine style
  - Fast competitions, for viewers to win something substantial

- There was a negative response to the following content:
  - Silly games
  - Adult presenters behaving like children
  - Competitions for studio guests

Our competitors fill this slot with cartoons, programmes aimed at the younger market and talk shows for adults We want a programme for the 13–16 audience.

What do you think? Write an outline of a TV programme that might be suitable for this audience and time slot.

(20 marks including 4 marks for spelling)

Reading and writing checklist

Reading

I am able to:

- Understand texts and find information in them ☐
- Describe what happens in a text ☐
- Select information to support my ideas ☐
- Provide quotations to support my ideas ☐
- Deduce and infer ideas from texts ☐
- Interpret texts to explain what an author means or wants us to think ☐
- Identify structural features such as connectives used to direct the reader ☐
- Explain how a text has been organised to direct the reader ☐
- Comment on presentation ☐
- Explain how writers have used language ☐
- Identify and explain writers' word choices ☐
- Identify and explain how writers have used techniques such as:
    - repetition ☐
    - rhetorical questions ☐
    - alliteration ☐
    - metaphor ☐
    - simile ☐
- Identify features that show what a writer's purpose is ☐
- Comment on a writer's purpose and viewpoint ☐
- Comment on the overall effect of the text on the reader ☐

Writing

I am able to:

- Write clearly and accurately, so my writing is easy to follow ☐
- Develop my writing in a thoughtful way ☐
- Match my writing to the intended audience ☐
- Match my writing to the purpose ☐
- Organise my writing so it makes sense and develops logically ☐
- Sequence my ideas for maximum impact on my reader ☐
- Write in clear paragraphs ☐
- Write in paragraphs that develop logically and make sense ☐
- Link my paragraphs using connectives ☐
- Use simple, compound and complex sentences to create maximum impact on my reader ☐
- Vary my sentences for clarity and purpose ☐
- Punctuate my sentences accurately ☐
- Choose appropriate and effective vocabulary ☐
- Use my imagination to write interesting texts ☐
- Use correct spelling ☐

The Shakespeare paper

The tasks

The Shakespeare task will be about the play and scenes you are studying.
You might be studying:
- *Richard III*
- *The Tempest*
- *Much Ado About Nothing.*

The task tests your reading and understanding of the play. This means it tests the same sort of skills as are assessed in the reading paper. You need to know the plot and who the main characters are. You also need to have studied your set scenes carefully. Your teacher will have told you what these are.

The questions

There are four sorts of question on the Shakespeare paper. These are on:

• Character and motivation
This means you have to understand the behaviour of the main characters.
You need to know and explain why the characters behave as they do.

• Ideas, themes and issues
This means you have to understand the particular ideas (such as love or revenge) that your play explores.

• The language of the text
This means looking at what Shakespeare's characters say, how they say it and the effect this has on the audience.

• The text in performance
This means understanding and explaining how the scenes would have been performed, and how you might put them on if you were the director.

Timing the test paper

• You have 45 minutes in total but you need to split this up to allow for planning and checking and improving. Spend the first 10 minutes planning your answer and the last 5 minutes checking and correcting it. This will leave you with 30 minutes to write it.

The questions in this Workbook

These questions have been written to allow you to answer them no matter which play you are studying or specific scenes you have been set.

This means you need to fill in some specifics:

Shakespeare question ← You will need to think about the play you have studied.

Key scenes: _____

_____

In the real test, specific extracts from your key scenes will be mentioned and included in your question paper. Make sure you know what these are and that you have a copy of them with you as you work through this section.

In these extracts, how is the idea of power explored through the main character?

← In the real test, the main character will be named.

Support your ideas by referring to both of the extracts which are printed on the following pages. ←

You are always required to refer to and quote from both extracts.

(18 marks)

Preparing for the Shakespeare test

1 Fill in the information:

The play I am studying: ─────────────────────────────

The key scenes I am studying: ─────────────────────────

The main characters in those scenes: ──────────────────

2 Character development

Track how each character changes on this emotion graph. Use a different colour for each character to make it clear. Caliban's changing emotions are shown on this graph as an example.

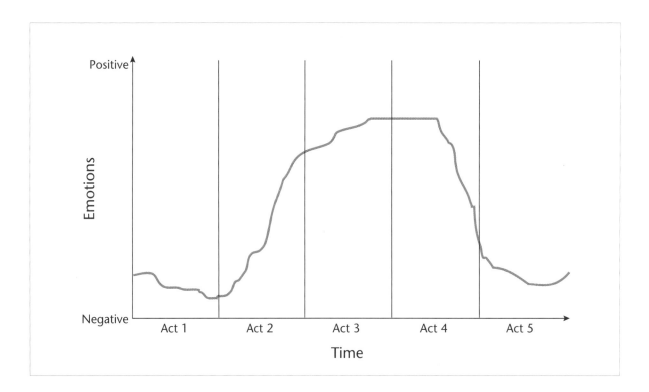

3 Character analysis

Many characters in Shakespeare's plays are like icebergs – they don't show everyone what they are really like. Complete an 'iceberg' for each of your main characters.

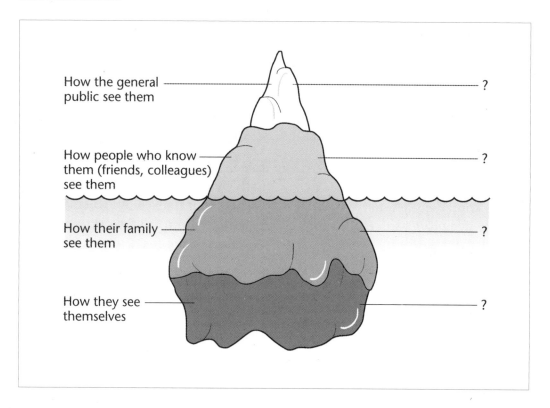

How the general public see them ——————————— ?

How people who know them (friends, colleagues) see them ——————————— ?

How their family see them ——————————— ?

How they see themselves ——————————— ?

Try to find quotations to support your ideas at each level.

4 Understanding the scenes

You've focused on the characters; now think about the way Shakespeare has structured the scenes. Fill in this tension graph for each of your key scenes.

Tension

High

Low

Time

Shakespeare's language

1 Match the meanings

Draw lines to match the modern English versions with these Shakespeare quotations.

The Tempest

Shakespeare's words	Modern version
1 If by your Art, my dearest father, you have Put the wild waters in this roar, allay them. The sky, it seems, would pour down stinking pitch, But that the sea, mounting to the welkin's cheek, Dashes the fire out.	A Make sure you stay invisible to do this task. Go to my house and get the bright and showy clothes and bring them here. They will be bait to catch these thieves.
2 If thou more murmur'st, I will rend an oak, And peg thee in his knotty entrails, till Thou hast howled away twelve winters.	B My dearest father, if you have used your magical Art to create this terrible storm, please calm the waters of the sea. It seems like the sky is pouring down molten tar which the sea rises up to put out.
3 Thy shape invisible retain thou still. The trumpery in my house, go bring it hither, For stale to catch these thieves.	C If you continue with your mutterings I will open up an oak tree and trap you inside it until you have howled for twelve years.

Richard III

Shakespeare's words	Modern version
1 Your Grace attended to their sugared words, But looked not on the poison of their hearts.	A We will unite the houses of York and Lancaster, as symbolised by the red and white roses. Heaven will smile at this union, especially after frowning for so long at the conflict that has been between them.
2 I think there's never a man in Christendom Can lesser hide his love or hate than he – For by his face straight shall you know his heart.	B I don't think you will be able to find any man in a Christian country who is less able to hide his love or hate than he is – you only have to look at his face to know what is in his heart.
3 We will unite the white rose and the red. Smile heaven upon this fair conjunction, That long have frowned upon their enmity!	C My Lord, you paid attention to their kind and attractive words and didn't see the poisonous nature of their hearts.

Much Ado About Nothing

Shakespeare's words	Modern version
1 Friendship is constant in all other things Save in the office and affairs of love. Therefore all hearts in love use their own tongues. Let every eye negotiate for itself, And trust no agent.	**A** Her personality is as stand-offish and wild as wild hawks that perch on rocks.
2 when Beatrice doth come, As we do trace this alley up and down, Our talk must only be of Benedick.	**B** Friendship is secure and reliable in everything except love. Anyone in love should follow their heart by themselves, without letting 'friends' help. You should not trust anyone but yourself.
3 her spirits are as coy and wild As haggards of the rock.	**C** We will walk up and down this path and, when Beatrice arrives, she will hear us talking of Benedick.

2 Analyse the language

Look at the quotations below. For each one, identify the language technique that has been used and explain the effect it has.

> simile   metaphor   alliteration   onomatopoeia   pun   rhyming couplet
> personification   antithesis   analogy   sibilance

Quotation	Technique	Effect
The Tempest 'the wild waters'	alliteration of 'w'	reflects the movement of the water
'The King's son, Ferdinand With hair up-staring – then like reeds, not hair – Was the first man that leaped'		
'The rarer action is In virtue than in vengeance.'		
Richard III 'I pray you all, tell me what they deserve That do conspire my death with devilish plots Of damned witchcraft'		
'Tut, tut, thou art all ice'		
Much Ado About Nothing 'doing in the figure of a lamb the feats of a lion'		
'being worthy to be whipped'		

Character and motivation

Choose the question that relates to the play you are studying. Use the space under the question to make notes and to write your plan. Write your actual answer on lined paper.

For more practice, you could have a go at answering the questions on the other plays. Just substitute the name of the character.

Top Tip!
You need to make sure you cover both the scenes you are directed to. It's a good idea to mention events and ideas from outside these scenes, but you must make sure your focus is on the scenes you are given.

The Tempest

Focus on the key scenes of your play.

What impression do you get of Caliban in these scenes?

Support your ideas by referring to **at least two** of the scenes you have studied in detail.

(18 marks)

Richard III

Focus on the key scenes of your play.

How does Richard change in these scenes?

Support your ideas by referring to **at least two** of the scenes you have studied
in detail.

(18 marks)

Much Ado About Nothing

Focus on the key scenes of your play.

How does Benedick change in these scenes?

Support your ideas by referring to **at least two** of the scenes you have studied
in detail.

(18 marks)

Themes

Choose the question that relates to the play you are studying. Use the space under the question to make notes and to write your plan. Write your actual answer on lined paper.

For more practice, you could have a go at answering the questions on the other plays. Just substitute the theme.

The Tempest

Focus on the key scenes of your play.

How is the idea of power and authority explored in these scenes?

Support your ideas by referring to **at least two** of the scenes you have studied in detail.

(18 marks)

Richard III

Focus on the key scenes of your play.

How is the idea of manipulation explored in these scenes?

Support your ideas by referring to **at least two** of the scenes you have studied in detail.

(18 marks)

Much Ado About Nothing

Focus on the key scenes of your play.

How is the theme of love explored in these scenes?

Support your ideas by referring to **at least two** of the scenes you have studied in detail.

(18 marks)

Language

Choose the question that relates to the play you are studying. Use the space under the question to make notes and to write your plan. Write your actual answer on lined paper.

For more practice, you could have a go at answering the questions on the other plays. Just substitute the name of the character.

The Tempest

Focus on the key scenes of your play.

The language in these scenes is used to create the personalities of the characters. Explain how the language is used to create the personality of at least one character.

Support your ideas by referring to **at least two** of the scenes you have studied in detail.

(18 marks)

Richard III

Focus on the key scenes of your play.

Richard's language is very striking and dramatic in these scenes. Explain how Shakespeare uses language to reveal Richard's character and personality in the scenes.

Support your ideas by referring to **at least two** of the scenes you have studied in detail.

(18 marks)

Much Ado About Nothing

Focus on the key scenes of your play.

The language used emphasises the high emotions in the scenes. Explain how Shakespeare has used language to create this emotion.

Support your ideas by referring to **at least two** of the scenes you have studied in detail.

(18 marks)

The text in performance

Choose the question that relates to the play you are studying. Use the space under the question to make notes and to write your plan. Write your actual answer on lined paper.

For more practice, you could have a go at answering the questions on the other plays. Just substitute the name of the character.

Top Tip!

Don't forget, this is **not** about saying you want an actor to 'move to the front of the stage and look upset' – it is focused on **language**, not movement.

The Tempest

Focus on the key scenes of your play.

Much of the comedy in this play comes from the sections with Stephano, Trinculo and Caliban. Imagine you are directing this play and explain how you want the actor playing Caliban to show his thoughts and emotions in these scenes.

Support your ideas by referring to **at least two** of the scenes you have studied in detail.

(18 marks)

Richard III

Focus on the key scenes of your play.

Richard is a very complex character. Imagine you are directing this play and the actor playing him is having difficulties. Explain how Richard should deliver his lines in these scenes.

Support your ideas by referring to **at least two** of the scenes you have studied in detail.

(18 marks)

Much Ado About Nothing

Focus on the key scenes of your play.

The relationship between Beatrice and Benedick is very important in this play. Imagine you are directing the play and explain how the actors playing these characters should show their thoughts and emotions in these scenes.

Support your ideas by referring to **at least two** of the scenes you have studied in detail.

(18 marks)

Practice Shakespeare paper

Try this practice Shakespeare paper.

Make sure you are in a quiet place and can spend 45 minutes without being disturbed.

You need to keep an eye on the time so that you spend 10 minutes planning, 30 minutes writing your answer and 5 minutes checking and improving.

- You will need your copy of the key scenes (but you will be provided with these in the real test).

- You will also need a pen and lined paper.

Shakespeare paper

This is worth 18 marks and you should spend 45 minutes on it.

This paper contains one task and you should answer it with reference to the key scenes of the Shakespeare play you have studied.

Answer the task that relates to the play you have studied.

The Tempest

Focus on the key scenes of your play.

What impression do you get of Stephano and Trinculo in these scenes?

Support your ideas by referring to **at least two** of the scenes you have studied in detail.

(18 marks)

Richard III

Focus on the key scenes of your play.

Richard uses language to try and get his own way. Explain how he uses language to try to persuade others in these scenes.

Support your ideas by referring to **at least two** of the scenes you have studied in detail.

(18 marks)

Much Ado About Nothing

Focus on the key scenes of your play.

Imagine you are directing this play. Explain how you want the actor playing Leonato to show his thoughts and emotions in these scenes.

Support your ideas by referring to **at least two** of the scenes you have studied in detail.

(18 marks)

You may use this page to plan your answer.

Shakespeare checklist

I am able to:

- Understand the events in the play ☐

- Understand the characters and their motivations ☐

- Describe what happens in my set scenes ☐

- Select key quotations to support my ideas ☐

- Make specific references to events in the play ☐

- Deduce and infer ideas from the events in the play ☐

- Identify structural features that add to the meaning of the play ☐

- Comment on stagecraft ☐

- Explain and comment on Shakespeare's use of language, including: ☐

  - metaphor ☐

  - simile ☐

  - alliteration ☐

  - onomatopoeia ☐

  - imagery ☐

  - repetition ☐

  - symbol ☐

- Explain the impact the text has on the audience ☐